W0007265

THE BRITISH PHONEBOX

Nigel Linge and Andy Sutton

AMBERLEY

To our respective wives, Joanne and Steph

Front and rear cover: Britain's quintessential red phonebox, a pre-1953 K6 kiosk, in the village of Kingham in the Cotswolds.

First published 2017

Amberley Publishing
The Hill, Stroud
Gloucestershire, GL5 4EP

www.amberley-books.com

Copyright © Nigel Linge and Andy Sutton, 2017

The right of Nigel Linge and Andy Sutton to be identified as the Authors of this work has been asserted in accordance with the Copyrights, Designs and Patents Act 1988.

ISBN 978 1 4456 6308 1 (print)
ISBN 978 1 4456 6309 8 (ebook)

All rights reserved. No part of this book may be reprinted or reproduced or utilised in any form or by any electronic, mechanical or other means, now known or hereafter invented, including photocopying and recording, or in any information storage or retrieval system, without the permission in writing from the Publishers.

British Library Cataloguing in Publication Data.
A catalogue record for this book is available from the British Library.

Typeset in 10pt on 13pt Celeste.
Origination by Amberley Publishing.
Printed in the UK.

Contents

Acknowledgements

In compiling this book, we are especially indebted to several people who have assisted us along the way. Firstly, Andrew Hurley, who provided us with unrivalled access to the National Telephone Kiosk collection held at Avoncroft Museum of Historic Buildings in Bromsgrove and who kindly gave constructive feedback on our draft manuscript. Secondly, Neil Johannessen, with his seemingly encyclopaedic knowledge of kiosks and his willingness to engage in informative and detailed email exchanges, has proved incredibly helpful in clarifying key dates and design details. Thirdly, David Hay and Dave Shawyer at BT Archives in London have been their usual extremely helpful selves and provided access to BT's comprehensive archives. Fourthly, Alison Taubman and Julia Orford, who kindly visited and photographed important kiosk sites in Scotland for us, and Jack Kirby, who kept his eyes peeled for unusual examples of adopted kiosks. Finally, we'd like to express our thanks to Dr Kin Wan, who kindly provided information about T-Mobile's use of GSM microcells in kiosks.

Chapter One

You May Telephone from Here

There are many icons and symbols that, when you see them, instantly remind you of a particular country. For Britain, these could be the Union Flag, the Houses of Parliament, the black cab, the red double-decker bus and, of course, the red phonebox – or, to use its more technical name, the red telephone kiosk. Wherever and whenever you see a red phonebox, you instantly think of Britain, which is quite remarkable, given that these icons of times past are rarely used today. Indeed, the vast majority of the younger generation have probably never set foot inside a phonebox, let alone used it for the purpose it was intended. Yet there it remains, resplendent as an essential part of what makes Britain, Britain!

In this book, we will be exploring the history and evolution of the humble British phonebox through all of its major versions, including those that were introduced by organisations such as the emergency services, those that have been given a new lease of life as something completely different, and the exciting new designs that, despite the all-encompassing mobile phone, are proving that the phonebox still has a future in twenty-first century Britain – albeit one in which they are no longer painted red. In so doing, we hope to instil an appreciation of this classic piece of telecommunications street furniture, to maybe even ignite feelings of nostalgia and to quite possibly turn you into a phonebox aficionado, meaning you'll no longer be able to walk along a street, or watch a television drama or film without immediately noticing and recognising a British phonebox. Enjoy!

Alexander Graham Bell submitted his patent for the telephone on St Valentine's Day, 1876, and just under one month later, on 10 March 1876, made the world's first telephone call while working with his assistant Thomas Watson, carrying out experiments in his Boston, Massachusetts, laboratory. The two men were in separate rooms, when Bell said, 'Mr Watson, come here, I want to see you'. Thomas Watson heard these immortal words on the primitive telephone they had developed and the rest, as they say, is history.

The telephone made its first appearance in Britain in September 1876, when Lord Kelvin displayed two non-working examples in Glasgow at a meeting of the British Association for the Advancement of Science. In the following year, William Preece, chief engineer at the British

Post Office, demonstrated a pair of working telephones in Plymouth. Alexander Bell, who was on honeymoon at the time, also attended that meeting and went on to deliver several lectures and demonstrations of his own throughout 1877. Perhaps the most prestigious of these was on Monday 14 January 1878, when Bell demonstrated his telephone to Queen Victoria at Osborne House on the Isle of Wight. Later that month, as reported in the Saturday 26 January 1878 edition of the *Manchester Weekly Times*, the first pair of telephones obtained by the Post Office from Bell's agent was installed in Manchester, linking Thomas Hudson's premises in Shudehill with those in Dantzic Street. This was typical of the early adopters, with telephones used as simple point-to-point communication devices. However, as their popularity grew, so the need arose for a telephone exchange that could connect any customer to any other. The Telephone Company opened Britain's first exchange at No. 36 Coleman Street in London in August 1879, shortly followed by the Lancashire Telephonic Exchange Company, who opened theirs in Faulkner Street in Manchester.

The formative years of the telephone in Britain are characterised by numerous separate, independent companies providing services within local geographic regions. Owning a telephone, however, was expensive. Customers with the United Telephone Company had to pay £20 per year, which, as one customer noted, was more expensive than employing your own telegraph boy to deliver messages for you. Naturally, these prices restricted the telephone to commercial users such as hotels, railway companies and shipping firms. Through a process of amalgamation, Britain's telephone companies were brought under the umbrella of the National Telephone Company with, following the Telegraph Act of 1892, the Post Office owning the national trunk network. Finally, the Telephone Transfer Act of 1911 brought the majority of telephone services within Britain into public ownership under the control of the Post Office, the district of Hull being a notable exception.

However, before these mergers were finalised, an important decision was taken in 1884 by the then Postmaster General, Henry Fawcett. Born in Salisbury in 1833, blinded in a shooting accident at the age of twenty-five and elected a Member of Parliament in 1865, Fawcett established himself as a powerful voice in support of women's suffrage. As Postmaster General, he is famed for the introduction of the parcel post, the postal order, the savings stamp and then, in 1884, for allowing telephone companies to build trunk lines connecting cities and to establish public call offices.

A fountain in Victoria Embankment Gardens dedicated to Henry Fawcett, the Postmaster General who introduced public call offices into Britain.

The public call office was the forerunner of the humble phonebox, and for the first time allowed access to the telephone service for non-subscribers in return for the payment of a small charge. This wasn't necessarily welcomed for, as one Edinburgh subscriber noted, 'any person off the street may, for a trifling payment, ring up any subscriber and insist on holding a conversation with him'. Companies did, however, respond positively to this new opportunity and began installing their own public call offices. No doubt they welcomed the additional revenue but also hoped that the experience of using a call office might encourage people to become subscribers. The Lancashire & Cheshire Telephonic Exchange Co., for example, opened call offices in Manchester, Liverpool, Blackburn and Preston. Subscribers to that company could be called by someone from a call office within the same town for a charge of three pence for three minutes. When available, calls from further afield were charged at the higher rate of six pence for three minutes but, calls to the fire service and local taxi firms and those in response to a medical emergency were free.

By 1886 seventy-five call offices were in use, located in places frequented by large numbers of people, such as railway stations, hotels and shops. However, shops weren't universally popular locations because people suspected that they would be encouraged to buy something when they had finished making a call. Some shop owners were accused of letting just their favoured customers use the telephone but, more importantly, the telephone was only accessible when the shop was open.

Call offices were rather basic in appearance and structure, often resembling a small wooden hut or sentry box, into which you stepped and closed the door behind you. The enclosed space not only offered privacy but also helped keep out unwanted noise, thereby resulting in them becoming known as silence cabinets. The telephone equipment within the call office had separate speaking and receiving parts, and all calls had to be connected via an operator. Payment was made by inserting coins into the telephone equipment, which caused an audible tone to be generated that the operator could hear. Many call offices also had a coin-operated lock on the door, while some were even staffed with an attendant, as in the case of the rather ornate cast-iron, free-standing, Persian-style call office opened in 1903 at Holborn, London. The attendant would greet you on arrival, take your payment, establish the call for you via the operator and then step outside while you had your conversation. However, there was always the suspicion that the attendant was listening in, and no doubt it was pretty unpleasant for them to be standing outside when it was pouring with rain.

A call office or, as it was sometimes known, a 'silence cabinet'. This example is preserved within the BT Archives, Holborn, London.

Typical telephone equipment found within an early call office. This example is within the call office preserved at BT Archives, Holborn, London.

The Holborn, cast-iron, Persian-style, attendant-operated call office, 1903.
(BT Heritage & Archives)

A rustic, arbour-style call office was installed in Blackburn in 1907. Sadly, it hasn't survived, but this model formed part of a limited edition collection of twelve Great British Phoneboxes produced by Scotland Direct.

Another elaborate design was the very ornate hexagonal rustic arbour installed at the tram terminus in Blackburn in 1907. It was large, measuring 6 feet 6 inches by 5 feet 8 inches at the base, and came equipped with an electric light, table and chairs. However, the table and chairs were soon removed, as it was discovered that the call office had become a refuge for men wanting to smoke cigarettes and play cards.

By 1907, the National Telephone Company operated 7,800 call offices throughout the country and their blue bell logo was often accompanied by the words: 'You may telephone from here'. In February of that year, the important role that a call office could play in society was aptly demonstrated when Josiah Mills, a labourer, was rescued from drowning in the freezing water of the River Wensum in Norwich. The newly installed call office on Norwich Thorpe railway station was used to summon help; a horse-drawn ambulance duly arrived and took the poor fellow to hospital, saving his life in the process. Also that year, the first case of vandalism to a call office was recorded. Angered that the operator had not heard him insert two pennies into the telephone equipment, Mr Samuel Wartski attempted to smash open the coin box. In doing so, he caused nineteen shillings worth of damage but was only fined one shilling as a rather sympathetic magistrate remarked that, 'telephones are frequently very troublesome and annoying to those that use them'.

National Telephone Company Blue Bell logo sign, indicating the location of a public call office.

An example of a typical 'You may telephone from here' sign, used to indicate the location of a public call office.

In these formative days of the phonebox, there was clearly a wide diversity in style and colour for Britain's growing population of call offices, but some common, all-wooden designs were beginning to emerge. The Norwich pattern, with its coin-operated door lock, was in common usage in East Anglia; the Wilson Company of Southsea produced its Wilson A pattern in large numbers; and the Birmingham pattern was commonly found in the Midlands.

However, with the onset of nationalisation, the General Post Office (GPO) decided that the time was right to seek a standard design for Britain's phoneboxes.

Above left: The Norwich pattern of call office was in common usage within East Anglia. (BT Heritage & Archives)

Above right: Wilson Company of Southsea produced the Wilson A call office pattern. (Neil Johannessen)

Left: Birmingham pattern of call office, with its characteristic lapped roof. (BT Heritage & Archives)

Chapter Two
Standardisation and the Design of an Icon

With the almost complete consolidation of the UK's telephone service in 1912 came a desire to standardise the design of public call offices. The underlying principles were that any new design should 'combine the aesthetic quality with economy of design and should be produced at no increase in cost over the existing types'. By 1914 two preliminary designs had been produced from within the GPO, but the intervention of the First World War put all such plans on hold. Phoneboxes based on the Birmingham pattern continued to be manufactured until January 1920, when a new design, which emanated from the earlier work, was finally approved by the GPO and given the designation 'K1'. The letter K referred to a kiosk and it is interesting to note that, although the word kiosk had been used previously, especially to describe free-standing, street-mounted public call offices, this is the first time that the term had been formally adopted.

By the time the K1 design was approved, concrete had become financially more viable than wood for their manufacture. Consequently, the new kiosk was made up of three sections of reinforced concrete and a wooden door. It measured 3 feet 0 inches square and 8 feet 8 inches tall but maintained a basic sentry-box styling. The door and two adjacent sides were half glazed, with the most common configuration comprising three rows of windows with two equal-sized windows at the top and bottom, and a single double-width pane of glass in the middle. This larger pane carried the words 'Public Telephone' and the smaller ones at the bottom, the words 'Open Always'. The rear of the kiosk was necessarily of solid construction for fixing of the telephone equipment and to allow the kiosk to be installed against a wall. The rear also had the words 'open' and 'always' painted on it. From this early stage, the GPO was mindful of the siting of kiosks, seeking to ensure that a kiosk was always visible without becoming an obstruction, while being close to an electricity supply. Finally, the K1 kiosk was topped off with a smooth pyramidal roof and orb finial. Generally, these early K1 kiosks were painted cream with a red door; the first version was known as a Mark 234. The K1 went into production in 1921 with an initial unit cost of £35 per kiosk, but this reduced to £13 as numbers increased.

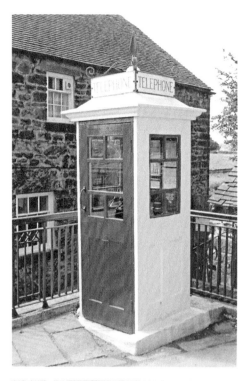

Kiosk K1, Mark 234, but fitted with the much later, more ornate roof decoration. This example is at the Crich Tramway Village. (Neil Johannessen)

Kiosk K1 Mark 235, but with a plain pyramidal roof. This example is on display at Avoncroft Museum of Historic Buildings.

A slight modification to the K1 design was introduced in 1922 with the K1 Mark 235. The most obvious difference was the adoption of a box structure added to the pyramidal roof, comprising a wrought-iron finial with scrolls placed above a metal 'Public Telephone' sign. No doubt this improved the overall visibility of the kiosk, and the new sign made its purpose clearer; however, it also increased the height of the kiosk by 1 foot, to 9 feet 8 inches. A further change, but one that's less obvious to the onlooker, was that the Mark 235 had metal window frames instead of the wooden ones used on the Mark 234. In fact, this is the only definitive way of distinguishing a Mark 234 from a 235, as there were many variations in the use of roof decoration across the two marks and this alone is, therefore, not sufficiently distinctive.

Local authorities were, however, reluctant to install kiosks unless they blended in with their environment; such attitudes not only limited kiosk deployment, especially in London, but also led to what must be one of the most bizarre kiosk configurations of all time. In July 1925, Eastbourne Corporation wanted two kiosks, one to be located at the Redoubt Bowling Green and the other at Hampden Park. These two sites were close to a bowling pavilion and a tea pavilion, both of which had thatched roofs. Consequently, the two K1s that were supplied came embellished with their own thatched roofs! Looking rather ungainly and top heavy, these were certainly unique kiosks, and, perhaps surprisingly, loved by at least one person who, many years later, in 1936, wrote the following letter to the *Eastbourne Chronicle*:

> Some years ago the Corporation persuaded the Post Office to put a miniature thatched top on the telephone kiosk, which stood at the corner of the Redoubt bowling green. The result was rather quaint for the box was a cross between a Chinese Pagola and a mushroom. Now I see that the thatched roof has gone and in its place is one of those horrible looking red phone boxes, which clashes with all the green hedges and grass. I hope that the Borough Surveyor hasn't given up on the fight for making things of utility, things of beauty too.

Despite this potential exception, the first standardised kiosk design was not well liked, especially by the Metropolitan Boroughs of London. Consequently, in 1923, the Metropolitan Boroughs Joint Standing Committee and the Birmingham Civic Society came up with their own competitive designs, which were presented to the GPO. While none were adopted, these initiatives did prompt the Postmaster General to task the Royal Fine Arts Commission to hold a design competition in

The Eastbourne thatched K1 Kiosk.
(BT Heritage & Archives)

Wooden prototype of Giles Gilbert
Scott's winning design for the K2 kiosk.
Now on display at the Royal Academy of
Arts, London.

May 1924. In addition to the designs already received, three notable architects were also invited to participate. These were Sir John Burnet, Sir Robert Lorimer and Giles Gilbert Scott. Wooden prototypes of each design were built and exhibited at a site close to the National Gallery in London, and it was Scott's design that was ultimately selected.

Giles Gilbert Scott was born on 9 November 1880 in Hampstead, London. His father was an accomplished architect and even more so his grandfather, Sir George Gilbert Scott, who had designed the Albert Memorial and St Pancras Hotel in London. Giles followed in their footsteps and, at the young and relatively inexperienced age of twenty-two, was awarded a contract to design Liverpool's Anglican Cathedral. This marked one of several iconic and high-profile commissions that he would undertake throughout his illustrious career. Others included the design of the library at the University of Cambridge, the New Bodleian Library in Oxford, Waterloo Bridge in London and both Battersea and Bank Side (now Tate Modern) power stations. Overall he worked on over forty ecclesiastical buildings, three cathedrals, twelve war memorials and forty other buildings of various types before his death on 8 February 1960. He was knighted by George V on 19 July 1924 at Knowsley Hall, near Liverpool, and is buried in the graveyard at Liverpool's Anglican Cathedral.

Scott's winning design therefore became Britain's second standardised kiosk, the K2, and offered a radical departure from anything that had gone before. It was a large kiosk, being 3 feet 4.5 inches square, 9 feet 3 inches tall, and was made from cast iron, except for the door, which was teak. Introduced onto the streets of London in 1925, each K2 weighed more than 1 ton and initially cost over £50. The door and two adjacent sides were glazed, with panels comprising six rows by three columns of equally sized rectangular windows. Its classical design comprises moulded column details down its edges, with horizontal moulding at the top below a back-illuminated, opaque, rectangular, glass telephone sign. Above that is a perforated Tudor crown, which provides ventilation for the kiosk. Finally, the kiosk is topped off by a domed roof, for which Scott took his inspiration from the Soane's family vault that lies within Old St Pancras churchyard in London. Sir John Soane was a renowned architect, being perhaps best known for designing the Bank of England. When his wife died in 1815, he designed her tomb as a lasting memorial and, following his own death in 1837, was interred there too. Giles Gilbert Scott was very familiar with this tomb, for he was a trustee of Sir John Soane's Museum, and the influence of its design is clear to be seen in the design of the K2, with its domed canopy resting atop of four ornate columns.

Left: Giles Gilbert Scott-designed K2 kiosk, on display at Avoncroft Museum of Historic Buildings.

Below: The much-photographed and delightful collection of five K2 Kiosks at Broad Court, Covent Garden, London.

Right: A K2 kiosk on Exhibition Road, London, near the Victoria and Albert Museum. Visible on the right-hand side of the kiosk are two holes caused by a bomb dropped during the Second World War.

Below: The classic design of the K2 involves moulded features, a back-illuminated glass telephone sign and a perforated Tudor Crown, which provides ventilation for the kiosk.

The Soane Memorial in Old St Pancras churchyard, which provided Giles Gilbert Scott with the inspiration for the design of the K2 kiosk's domed roof.

Although Scott wanted his kiosk to be painted silver with a greenish-blue interior, the GPO adopted vermillion for the outside and flame for the interior, except for the underside of the roof, which was painted white, no doubt to reflect more of the light from the lightbulb. Despite its classic design and imposing appearance, the K2 was deemed to be too large and expensive for general use and so tended to be mainly installed within London, with only a few examples appearing in other cities. To cater for the remainder of the country, the GPO turned its attention back to the K1. Remodelled as the Mark 236, this third version of the K1 appeared in 1927, retaining its original basic dimensions and construction but with a new fuller-height window configuration, comprising four rows of two equally sized windows in each side. The door had seven panes of glass: six smaller ones as per the side panels, with one double-width one. In 1928 the door was changed to be the same configuration as the side panels and then, in 1929, the plain pyramidal roof had ornate wrought-iron work added as per the K1 Mark 235, but with reduced signage where 'Public Telephone' was replaced with the simpler 'Telephone'.

Interestingly, in among this drive for standardisation, there still remained the opportunity for unique kiosk designs to emerge. As an illustration of this, in 1928 Scottish architect John Fraser designed a concrete kiosk for Pittencrieff Park in Dunfermline. Seemingly the motivation for providing this kiosk was that placing a telephone in the nearby tea rooms, which Fraser also designed, would have become a nuisance to the patrons. While appearing to be made of dressed stone, this kiosk was in fact manufactured from concrete, except for the wooden door, and featured a copper-clad, bell-shaped roof,

Above: The internal roof detail of a K2 kiosk, showing the ventilation grille and light.

Right: A K1 kiosk, Mark 236, with the original 1927 door configuration but the 1929 ornate roof decoration. This example is on display at Avoncroft Museum of Historic Buildings.

The concrete, John
Fraser-designed
unique kiosk at
Pittencrieff Park
in Dunfermline.
(Julie Orford)

finished off with a timber finial. While distinctive, it is unlikely that
this kiosk was ever officially adopted by the GPO, remaining instead
a private kiosk to which the GPO had provided a telephone service. It
is, however, still standing today and has the honour of being one of
Scotland's smallest listed buildings.

Still seeking a cheaper kiosk for widespread deployment than the
K2, but one that was more decorative than the K1, the GPO turned
once again to Sir Giles Gilbert Scott, who was awarded a contract
to design a new concrete kiosk. No doubt the adoption of concrete
necessitated a plainer design than the K2, but much of its elegance
was retained in the K3, which became available in 1928. Shorter and
narrower than the K2, the K3 measured 3 feet 1 inch square by 8 feet
7.5 inches tall and was made of three concrete sections with a teak
door. The door and two adjacent sides were glazed, with six rows of
three equally sized rectangular windows and a domed roof raised
above the main body of the kiosk to create ventilation slots. Gone
is the royal crown, but the back-illuminated telephone sign on opal
glass was retained. The K3 was stipple painted in Clipsham stone
colour, giving the kiosk a rougher surface texture. Red was, however,
retained for painting the window glazing bars. Launch of the K3
brought a halt to the use of the K1, and it remained the standard
GPO kiosk until 1936. Sadly, few of these K3 kiosks have survived,
with one in the hamlet of Rhynd in Scotland, one overlooking the
Penguin Beach at London Zoo, one on display at Avoncroft Museum

Above: Roof detail of the K3 kiosk, showing how it is raised above the main body of the kiosk to create ventilation slots. This example is on display at Avoncroft Museum of Historic Buildings.

Right: The surviving K3 kiosk in the hamlet of Rhynd in Scotland. (Andrew Lee)

The surviving K3 kiosk, opposite the Penguin Beach at London Zoo.

of Historic Buildings in Bromsgrove and one known to be in private ownership being rare exceptions.

Without doubt, the largest kiosk to ever grace Britain's streets was the K4, introduced in 1927. This leviathan of a kiosk measured 3 feet 4.5 inches wide by 4 feet 4.5 inches long by 9 feet 3 inches tall and in effect extended a K2 to incorporate a mini-post office, comprising a letter box and two stamp-issuing machines. Originally these issued one half and one full pre-decimal penny stamps, with the coins being collected in a leather-lined box located below the letter box. Designed by the GPO's engineering department, it brought to fruition ideas that were first proposed in 1923. Painted vermillion on the outside and flame inside, it was thought that combining telephone and postal services within a single kiosk would avoid the GPO having to open sub-post offices where this might be uneconomical.

However, the sheer size of the K4 was its downfall, as siting it proved extremely problematic. Without a blank side or the option of relocating the door, it was difficult to position a K4 against a wall. Equally, putting it on a pavement took up so much room that the GPO received complaints from pedestrians, who said it caused an obstruction, and drivers who felt it restricted their vision. In addition to this, there were reports of operational problems in terms of the reliability of the stamp-issuing machines and noise generated from using the post office. Consequently, only fifty were made, but several

The K4 kiosk at Frodsham, Cheshire, looking at the telephone side with the door on the left-hand side of the photograph.

The K4 kiosk at Frodsham, Cheshire, looking at the Post Office side, with its two stamp-dispensing machines (blanked off) and letter box.

have survived. The example in Frodsham, Cheshire, is now listed and serves to illustrate what a dominant presence the K4 had on our streets.

Another unusual kiosk design was that of the K5. Not intended for permanent installation, the K5 was in fact a flat-packed, pop-up kiosk that could be used in temporary locations, for example, at events and exhibitions. It was constructed from steel-faced plywood with a general outline similar to the K3, but with a window arrangement reminiscent of the early marks of the K1. Designed by the GPO's engineering department in 1934, the K5 comprised seven pieces that could be packed into three cases for transportation. Sadly, no original examples have survived but there is an accurate replica on show at Avoncroft Museum of Historic Buildings in Bromsgrove.

By 1935 the GPO had installed nearly 20,000 kiosks, with the most numerous being the K3; the K2 continued to be mainly restricted to London. However, it was also becoming apparent that, while cast iron was more expensive to manufacture, it was far more durable, with concrete proving to be fragile during transportation, less weather resistant and more difficult to keep clean. Equally, the walls of concrete kiosks are thicker, which restricts their usable internal space. Consequently, the forthcoming Silver Jubilee of George V provided the perfect catalyst for the GPO to reappraise the design of its standard kiosk.

A close-up of the internal workings of one of the K4 kiosk's stamp-dispensing machines, which were reported as being unreliable and noisy.

Opening the letter box on the K4 Kiosk reveals a sign telling the postman to 'Shut door quietly'! Note also that the open coin drawer at the bottom is leather lined, so as to reduce noise.

The replica, flat-packed K5 kiosk on display at Avoncroft Museum of Historic Buildings.

Chapter Three

The Red Box

While the designs covered in the previous chapters are all important in the story of the British phonebox, it is perhaps the version designed in 1935 that is, for many, Britain's ubiquitous red box. George V ascended the British throne on 6 May 1910 and was crowned on 22 June 1911 at Westminster Abbey. His Silver Jubilee of 1935, therefore, provided the GPO with a high-profile occasion to celebrate through the launch of a new standard kiosk. By 1935 the GPO still didn't have a single standard kiosk that was acceptable throughout the country. The K2 was mainly deployed in London but was deemed too big for general use, whereas the K3 was more usefully proportioned and widely deployed but lacked some of the finesse of the K2; its concrete construction was also proving less durable. What was needed was a new design that combined the elegance and durability of the K2 with the dimensions of the K3. This was the challenge given to Sir Giles Gilbert Scott, whose response would result in a design that not only epitomises the quintessential British phonebox but that has also become a lasting symbol of the country itself.

This new design became the GPO's sixth kiosk – hence K6 – but has become commonly known as the Jubilee kiosk. More importantly, the K6 was in fact Britain's first truly standard kiosk, for it could genuinely be found everywhere, from the largest city to the smallest village. Like the K2, the K6 was constructed from cast iron, except for the door, which was teak. Its door and adjacent sides were glazed but, unlike the K2, the K6's windows comprised a broad central pane with narrow ones either side, organised in eight, not six, rows. The top of the K6 was plainer than that of the K2, comprising a telephone sign on opaque glass surrounded by simple moulding, below which was a slot for ventilation, as per the K3, and, above it, a moulded royal crown. Clearly the influence of the Soane memorial was still strong, as evidenced by the domed roof. Overall the K6 was noticeably smaller than the K2 and fractionally smaller than the K3, being 3 feet 0.25 inches square and 8 feet 4 inches tall. It was also considerably lighter, weighing 0.68 metric tons, and could be erected in a single day.

Having approved the design in 1935, the GPO planned to roll out the K6 from January 1936. A test prototype was installed in London in December 1935 and, by February 1936, supplies of this new kiosk started to arrive. However, it was not until July of that year that the K6 became available to the GPO in large numbers, thereby allowing a full-scale deployment to commence.

Right: The Sir Giles Gilbert Scott-designed K6 kiosk.

Below: The domed roof of the K6 kiosk, clearly showing the continued influence of the Soane memorial, the ventilation slots below the 'Telephone' sign and the embossed Tudor Royal Crown. But has an act of heresy been committed by painting this crown gold?

These K2 kiosks, which sandwich a pair of K6 kiosks on Carey Street, London, allow you to compare the relative sizes of each design.

The GPO's telephone service instructions of the day gave very clear advice on how to select the best site for a kiosk. These included choosing prominent locations that offered easy access for the public and a high likelihood of generating revenue. To minimise the risk of malicious damage, it was advised to place kiosks where they were most frequently under observation by the police or other responsible persons. Even the prevailing wind was taken into consideration to ensure that it always acted in such a manner as to close the door. Perhaps not too surprisingly, it was suggested that a site over a cellar, or other underground chamber, should be avoided where possible and that kiosks should not be erected under trees or in excessively noisy environments. Naturally, where high levels of demand were anticipated, several kiosks would be installed, either in a row or small cluster. One important factor that, of course, still governs kiosk locations today is the availability of a suitable electricity supply.

Linked to the launch of the K6, the GPO introduced the Jubilee Concession Scheme, which pledged to provide a kiosk for every town and village that had a post office but where there wasn't already a kiosk within half a mile's walking distance, irrespective of the anticipated income it might generate. More than 1,000 K6s were installed under this scheme, which was followed by the Tercentenary Concession that celebrated the 300th anniversary of the Post Office. Here the GPO agreed to provide a kiosk in any rural village or hamlet where it couldn't be justified by the number of calls, providing the local authority would agree to pay an annual fee of £4 for five years.

Where space permitted and demand was high, kiosks could also be arranged in clusters, as per this example of four K6s in Cheltenham.

The interior of the kiosk was also redesigned and standardised. On the back wall of the kiosk, above the level of the telephone itself, were placed five stainless steel notice frames, mounted on a Bakelite-covered plywood board. On the left was a long, rectangular frame that contained instructions on how to use the telephone, while on the far right was a frame of the same size, which included information on call charges. Between these two were three smaller frames, arranged one above the other. The one at the top was a publicity notice, below which was a mirror, and then at the bottom an emergency services call notice. In subsequent years, this arrangement was modified so that the small notice frames were replaced with a third long frame that matched those either side of it, with the emergency services call notice being placed below them and to the right. If you could remove this plywood backboard then there is often a date of manufacture for the kiosk hidden behind it, embossed within its casting.

A 200 series Bakelite telephone was fitted to the top of a shelf unit, into which callers could temporarily place parcels or a handbag. Further to the right was another shelf unit for storing printed telephone directories. Initially, this included a hook for holding an

The original standard interior configuration of a K6 kiosk, showing five notice frames with two shelf units placed either side of the A/B coin box.

The modified interior configuration of a K6 kiosk, comprising three rectangular notice frames and a re-positioned emergency services call notice.

umbrella but the shelf was later widened, forcing the removal of the hook. Between the two shelf units was the standard A/B pre-payment coin box. Callers had to insert the correct money before making their call. Once answered, button A was pressed to connect the call or button B was pressed to return their money.

A rather interesting feature to the right of the telephone was a stainless-steel, open-grille tray into which could be placed a lighted cigarette or pipe. The open grille allowed any ash to fall on the floor; how times have changed!

However, perhaps the most burning question was what colour should be used for the standard kiosk. When launched in 1936, the K6 was painted Post Office red but there were objections to this. The primary reason why the GPO chose red was 'to ensure that a kiosk could be readily distinguishable from its surroundings so as to be recognised from a distance by a stranger in the stress of an emergency which in turn demanded a uniformity of colour throughout the country'. One critic of this policy said that the natural beauty of rural settings 'was to be sacrificed to motorists who were half an hour late for dinner and wanted to telephone home so that the soup could be kept warm'. In response to criticism of this type, the GPO approached the Royal Fine Arts Commission for their opinion on the colour issue and in 1939 they endorsed the GPO's current practice. However, under pressure from the Council for the Preservation of Rural England, they conceded that special cases might be made for areas of outstanding

The open stainless-steel grille tray to the right of the 200 series Bakelite telephone, on to which callers could place their lighted cigarettes or pipe.

natural beauty, where a kiosk could be painted dark grey, with red only being used on the window glazing bars.

Despite this decision, the issue rumbled on and, following questions being raised in the House of Lords, the Postmaster General brought together in 1947 the Ministry of Town and Country Planning, the Royal Fine Arts Commission and the Council for the Preservation of Rural England to examine six kiosks, painted in a range of colour schemes. One was painted in Post Office red, one in deep Brunswick green, one in middle Brunswick green, one in black, one in light battleship grey and the final one in dark battleship grey. The non-red kiosks also had the window glazing bars on the door and one side painted red to provide a further set of paint schemes to examine. Finally, the conclusion reached was to maintain red as the standard colour, with the proviso that dark battleship grey with red glazing bars could be adopted in rural locations.

There was, of course, part of the country where these rules didn't apply. Telephone services within Hull remained under the control of Hull Corporation and were therefore independent of the GPO. Consequently, while Hull installed K6 kiosks, theirs were painted cream and didn't carry a royal crown. Today, telecommunications services in Hull are provided by the privatised KCOM group, formerly Kingston Communications, but fortunately some of their K6s have

A K6, painted in the rural colour scheme of dark battleship grey with red window glazing bars. This example is on display at Avoncroft Museum of Historic Buildings.

While adopting the K6 kiosk but being independent of the GPO, Hull painted their kiosks cream and omitted the Royal Crown.

Hull's Bee Box on the right, painted in tribute to Jean Bishop, who won a Pride of Britain Award for her fourteen years of fundraising for Age UK; all of it done wearing a bee costume!

survived. One took on a most unusual colour scheme in October 2013, when it was painted black and gold in tribute to Jean Bishop, who won a Pride of Britain Award for her fourteen years of fundraising for Age UK. Jean is famous throughout Hull for the bee costume she wears when raising money.

Unlike the K2, the crown on the K6 kiosk was moulded rather than perforated and came in three versions. From 1935 to 1953 the Tudor Crown was used on all state documents and by all government departments and, hence, on kiosks. However, with the coronation of Elizabeth II in 1953, this was changed to the St Edward's Crown. From 1955, kiosks installed in Scotland carried a representation of the Crown of Scotland and, to accommodate this, kiosks produced from 1955 onwards were cast with slots into which the appropriate crown could be inserted. However, one of the most controversial aspects of the crown is the recent trend when refurbishing kiosks to paint the crowns gold. In their heyday, crowns on kiosks were always painted red as per the box. Quite when and why a fashion for painting crowns gold began is not known but, for the purist, there is no debate: crowns should always be red and painting them gold is nothing short of heresy! We'll leave it to you to decide where your loyalties lie on this particular one.

While often inaccessible, the rear of a K6 can provide some very useful information about the kiosk. There are two versions of the K6 – a mark 1 and mark 2. The mark 1 suffered from two major problems and these were, firstly, that the glass panels could be easily removed and, secondly, that the coin box was susceptible to theft. So, in 1939, the mark 2 was introduced, in which the window glazing frames were riveted into place and a new, more secure fixing was used for the coin box. You can differentiate these by looking at the cable entry holes at the bottom of the rear panel of the kiosk. If these holes are equally spaced from the edges of the kiosk, then it's a mark 1, but, if they are of unequal distances, in effect shifted to the right, then it's the later and more numerous mark 2. Also, between these two holes is the maker's plate, which identifies the place of manufacture. In total, five foundries manufactured the K6 kiosk and all but one was in Scotland. These were the Carron Foundry in Falkirk, the Lion Foundry in Kirkintilloch, the McDowall Steven Foundry in Port Dundas, the Macfarlane (also known as Saracen) Foundry in Glasgow and Bratt Colbran in London. However, Bratt Colbran only made mark 1 kiosks and we believe that their boxes didn't carry a maker's plate.

Over 65,000 K6 kiosks were manufactured, making it Britain's definitive and most recognised red box – so much so that today you regularly see its image adorning postcards, Christmas cards, coffee

Crowns on the K6 kiosk were moulded, rather than perforated as in the case of the K2. The top image is the Tudor Crown, used between 1936 and 1953. The middle image shows St Edward's Crown, which was introduced in 1953, while the bottom image shows the 1955 modification whereby the crown was slotted into the kiosk.

An example of a K6 installed in Scotland, where a representation of the Scottish Crown is used. (Andrew Lee)

mugs, badges, coasters and a whole host of memorabilia and ephemera. Today, with our heightened appreciation of heritage and nostalgia, the K6 kiosk has become fashionable and even loved. However, this wasn't always the case, for in reality the K6 was proving increasingly expensive to maintain, the costs of vandalism were growing and the design wasn't well suited for disabled access. Equally, as Britain left behind the austerity of the post-war years and headed towards the swinging sixties, so came a thirst and drive for modernity that sought to sweep away the old for a new and exciting future. Wrapped up in this euphoria was the humble phonebox, where the K6 was now viewed as belonging to the past and, therefore, ripe for replacement with something far more modern in appearance and design.

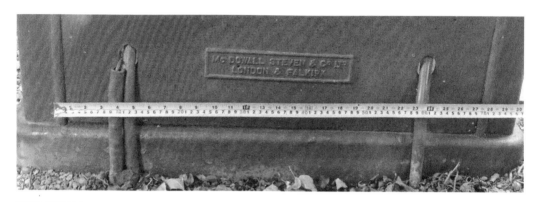

The rear of a K6 provides some useful information about the kiosk. The top image is a mark 1, identifiable because the cable entry holes are the same distance in from each side, whereas the bottom image is a mark 2 because the cable entry holes are clearly offset to the right. The maker's plate confirms that the top kiosk was made by McDowall Steven & Co. Ltd and the bottom kiosk by the Lion Foundry.

Chapter Four

Modernisation and Privatisation

Towards the end of the 1950s, the GPO was once again reappraising its standard kiosk design. While the K6 had served it well, the country was now looking forward and embracing its new modernist, concrete town-centre landscapes and, for those, a kiosk was needed that reflected the future, not the past. So, in 1959, the GPO turned to architect Neville Conder. Awarded the CBE for his design of the Ismaili Centre in Kensington, Neville Conder was a highly influential figure in post-war British architecture.

His resulting design for a telephone kiosk was undoubtedly modern, with its large windows, chamfered corners, a narrow concrete base that gave the impression the whole kiosk was floating above the ground, and the use of aluminium instead of cast iron. Emerging as the K7 in 1962, six prototypes of Conder's design were put on trial in London and Coventry, and a further six were also manufactured by the GPO but using cast iron. Unfortunately, the British climate soon turned the untreated aluminium a streaky grey-black with white blisters, and this rapidly dissuaded the GPO from putting the K7 into production. Consequently, the K7 is Britain's least numerous kiosk design, for it never evolved beyond the prototype stage. Quite what happened to the cast-iron examples of the K7 isn't known, but a rare surviving example of the aluminium K7 forms part of the National Telephone Kiosk collection at the Avoncroft Museum of Historic Buildings.

Aside from problems with aluminium and the desire to modernise its kiosks, the GPO was trying to cope with another pressing matter and that was the growing problem of kiosk vandalism. Speaking in the House of Commons in January 1966, the Postmaster General, Tony Benn MP, estimated that the total cost of kiosk vandalism was £200,000 for the previous year. He went on to state that kiosks were being vandalised as quickly as they could be repaired. Consequently, the sheer scale of the problem caused a temporary shortage of replacement parts, which, in turn, meant that some kiosks were out of commission for up to three months.

The average cost of installing a kiosk in 1966 was £410, with an annual running cost, excluding depreciation, interest and vandalism repair of between £70 and £75 per year. In 1965, the GPO reported that its kiosk business was running at a loss of £4.2 million, or

A surviving example of the six K7 prototypes that were manufactured. This example is on display at Avoncroft Museum of Historic Buildings.

approximately £55 per kiosk per year. With such a deficit, the GPO was keen to minimise any further losses incurred due to vandalism.

Earlier, in 1965 on 23 March, in response to a question in Parliament, Tony Benn confirmed that the GPO was in the process of commissioning designs for a new but more vandal-resistant kiosk. In fact, the GPO had invited Neville Conder, Douglas Scott and Bruce Martin to submit designs. Whether his earlier experience with the K7 had any bearing on the matter or not, Neville Conder withdrew, leaving Scott and Martin. Douglas Scott was one of the country's first professional industrial designers, who had worked on iconic products such as the Aga cooker and London's Routemaster bus. Bruce Martin, on the other hand, was an architect who pioneered the modular approach to building design. Full-size prototypes of each of their kiosks were examined by the GPO and, in May 1966, it was Martin's design that was chosen, thus becoming Britain's eighth standard kiosk – the K8.

The K8 was hailed as a masterpiece of industrial design with its modern style, clean, and uncluttered look. While Martin had planned for his kiosk to be made from aluminium, the GPO changed this to cast iron with the exception of the door, which was kept as aluminium to reduce weight. Its full-height single toughened glass rectangular windows were designed to reduce vandalism, as the perpetrator could be more easily seen. Instead of a dome, the K8 had a flattened box roof with slightly tapered sides that each contained a glazed 'Telephone' sign but, interestingly, no crown. Originally this roof section was going to be made of fibreglass so that it would shine like a beacon when illuminated from the internal fluorescent light.

However, it proved impossible to get the correct consistency in the fibreglass and so, in the end, the roof too was made from cast iron. Having carefully studied the design of the K6, Martin dramatically reduced the number of component parts required to build his K8, and ensured that all fixings were hidden from view. Ventilation was provided via a gap at floor level and another between the roof section and main body of the kiosk. Like the K7, the K8's narrow base gave the impression of the kiosk floating above the ground. Additionally, the prefabricated modular design allowed the K8 to be installed in any configuration, with the door, side and back panels being placed in the most appropriate position to suit the location. In keeping with its modern design, the official dimensions of the K8 were quoted metrically, with the kiosk being 2,450 mm tall and 900 mm square. The paint scheme was also changed, with the old Post Office red being replaced by a new, more vibrant shade called Poppy Red. The first K8 was installed at Nos 6–7 Old Palace Yard, Westminster, on 12 July 1968, and thereafter replaced the K6 as the standard kiosk.

Above left: The Bruce Martin-designed K8 kiosk was a significant departure from the K6, with its new modern styling. This example is on display at Milton Keynes Museum.

Above right: This K8 in Highworth, Wiltshire, is a rare survivor of its type and has now been officially listed.

In 1971, the Lion Foundry contacted the GPO concerning problems with the design and casting of the K8 roof section. The glazed telephone signs were proving difficult to mould and the thin metal section of the roof tended to crack on cooling. Consequently, a new casting was proposed, in which the telephone sign was surrounded by a thicker moulding that flowed as a continuous curve from the bottom of the roof section. This new design was approved by the GPO and generally adopted from 1976, thereby providing a mechanism for dating a K8. During its production run, a total of 11,000 K8 kiosks were manufactured and installed, but little was it realised at the time that the K8 would ultimately be remembered as Britain's last red phonebox.

In November 1972, Sir John Eden, Minister of Posts and Telecommunications, confirmed in the House of Commons that, out

The roof of the K8 was made of cast iron, rather than fibreglass, with the telephone signs being illuminated by an internal fluorescent light. The top image shows the original roof design, comprising a simple oval moulding around the glazed telephone sign. The bottom image is of the modified roof design, introduced in 1976 to overcome difficulties with moulding the telephone sign and to prevent cracking in the casting when being cooled.

of a total of 76,000 kiosks, 3,700 were of the new, improved design. Earlier in the year his predecessor, Mr Chataway, reported that there had been a reduction in incidents of kiosk vandalism in the twelve months up to the end of September 1971, with 150,027 in comparison to the 171,044 previously. However, by 1973, the costs of damage to kiosks was still running at £473,000 annually, thereby proving that, despite the improvements in design offered by the K8, vandalism to kiosks continued to be a major problem and much of that had its roots in an earlier technological innovation.

In 1958, the national telephone service was upgraded through the introduction of subscriber trunk dialling, which allowed people to directly dial other parts of the country without the need for the intervention of a human operator. Naturally, this had implications for kiosks in that, if callers were now able to dial longer distances, then call charges must similarly increase. Consequently, the existing pre-payment A/B button coin-collecting box was replaced with a new pay-on-answer telephone 705. Now, when you wanted to make a call, you first dialled the other person and only inserted coins once they answered. Thereafter your call was timed and, when charging limits were reached, you were prompted by a series of audible beeps, normally called pips, to insert more coins. Failure to do so resulted in the call being automatically terminated. Because you only inserted coins when the call was connected, there was now no need for any buttons to press for returning your coins. This did mean that, once coins had been inserted, they couldn't be returned to the caller, except in circumstances where damaged coins were detected, in which case they were returned via a slot at the bottom of the unit. Inevitably, with more money now being held within the kiosk, this made them more attractive to thieves and, very quickly after its introduction, a new armoured version of the telephone 705 had to be introduced, which was made from heavy-gauge steel. Naturally, further modifications were required to these telephone systems, as the country switched to decimal currency on 15 February 1971.

On 1 October 1969, the GPO ceased to be a government department and was established as a nationalised industry under the Post Office Act, with two distinct divisions, one concerned with postal services and the other with telecommunications. Post Office Telecommunications became British Telecom in 1980 and was then completely separated from the Post Office in 1981, before eventually being privatised in 1984 and then trading as simply BT from 1991.

For British Telecom, where incidents of vandalism were particularly high, a radical approach was adopted wherein the existing kiosk was removed and replaced with the Oakham Booth 7A, which was first

Above left: The 705 pay-on-answer telephone and coin box, which replaced the old A/B button coin collecting box.

Above right: The armoured version of the Telephone 705. Note the protruding coin box at the bottom.

Left: The Oakham Booth 7A pedestal kiosk, installed in areas suffering from high levels of kiosk vandalism. This example is on display at Avoncroft Museum of Historic Buildings.

introduced in Gateshead in 1980. This pedestal kiosk was nothing more than a telephone on a stick, enclosed by an open but sturdy metal surround. The shape of this surround is how this particular kiosk design got its name, as it resembled a tin of Olde Oak ham. However, more striking was the choice of colour. Bright yellow replaced the traditional red to correspond with the corporate branding of British Telecom, which used a combination of yellow and blue. However, concerns that British Telecom might extend this practice with a wider adoption of yellow caused Mr Kenneth Baker, Minister of Information Technology within the Department of Industry, to be asked in the House of Commons on 9 February 1981 whether he was aware that 'British Telecom is investing a certain amount of money in yellow paint at the moment, with a view to painting telephone kiosks yellow?'

There was indeed truth in this rumour, for British Telecom did start painting some of its kiosks yellow. This in turn caused outrage. The *Daily Mail* newspaper began a national campaign against the 'yellow peril' and, fortunately, British Telecom soon saw the error of its ways and the practice stopped.

An example of a kiosk from the Croydon range. (BT Heritage & Archives)

Nevertheless, British Telecom was keen to address its lossmaking kiosk business and find a new design that was both cheaper to manufacture and maintain. A further consideration was to ensure that its kiosks offered better access to people with disabilities; callers had to negotiate a step, for example, to enter a K6 or K8 kiosk.

Various designs were considered, including several imported from overseas. However, perhaps the largest-scale trial was the so-called Croydon range, developed in-house within British Telecom. An order for seventy-five units was placed in 1981/82, with kiosks being installed in Leicester Square and Oxford Street in London and phone booths being erected at Bristol Temple Meads railway station. These designs didn't, however, progress beyond this initial trial stage.

As an alternative to completely new designs, British Telecom also started to modify existing kiosks, where, for example, the small windows of a K6 were replaced with a large toughened glass pane like the K8. Thankfully, this wasn't too widespread, for the result was a rather ugly creation that many regarded as being a borderline case of corporate vandalism against a design icon.

Britain's public payphone system in the mid-1980s was in trouble. It had been lossmaking for years; vandalism continued to be a major problem; reliability was poor; and attempts to modify kiosks hadn't been well received. Something had to be done and, in 1985, British Telecom announced a £160 million investment programme to provide an efficient and more reliable payphone service. A key part of this was a new generation of kiosks that was trumpeted as 'payphones for the twenty-first century'. These new kiosks were designed to be modern,

Payphones for the 21st Century: the front cover of the launch-day press pack, 20 June 1985. (Neil Johannessen)

46

easier to keep clean, cheaper to maintain, more resilient to vandalism and provide better access to people with disabilities. The first one was unveiled to the public in London's Leicester Square on 20 June 1985.

This new kiosk range was manufactured by the British company GKN. Stainless steel, anodised aluminium and toughened glass were used to combat vandalism, but also to reduce maintenance costs, as their finishes were more durable, didn't require painting and retained their appearance with minimal cleaning. In addition, improved access for the elderly and people with disabilities was provided by reducing the height of the telephone and removing obstacles to wheelchairs. Known as the KX range, it included the KX100, which was a full kiosk that could be supplied with or without a door. The door and adjacent sides comprise large glass panels set in a metal frame with a central horizontal bar. Signage and company logos are printed on the glass panels, which were originally smoked glass but subsequently changed to clear. A large gap at the bottom prevents the accumulation of litter and a smaller gap at the top aids ventilation. The roof is flat and the door opens fully to allow wheelchair access.

The KX200 is a large pedestal kiosk, with side and top panels forming a protective hood around the telephone itself. However, this

A KX100 kiosk, one of the new standard range introduced from 1985. This particular one is in Willington, County Durham, and replaced a K6 red phonebox that had stood on that site previously.

Above left: The KX200 kiosk, also part of the new standard range introduced from 1985, was designed to give easy access to wheelchair users.

Above right: Another example of the standard range of kiosks introduced from 1985 is this KX300 triangular open-kiosk design.

Left: This KX420 pedestal kiosk also formed part of the standard range of kiosks introduced from 1985. (Neil Johannessen)

hood stops well short of the floor to allow a wheelchair user full access. The KX300 is an unusual triangular design. Supplied without a door, one of the glazed sides could be replaced by a solid one with storage for directories. Like the KX100, there was a large gap between the bottom of the side panels and the floor. Finally, the KX420 was a pedestal kiosk.

One consequence of these modernisation plans was that British Telecom intended to replace their existing stock of kiosks as well as seeking to install kiosks in totally new locations. The Twentieth Century Society, then known as the Thirties Society, became extremely concerned about this impending threat to the country's red phoneboxes and intervened by writing to every local authority, urging them to voice their objections and help protect these fine examples of British industrial design. The society published their report, 'The British Telephone Box – Take it as Red' and urged the Department of the Environment to formally list kiosks as historically important miniature buildings. While this achieved success in protecting examples of both the K2 and K6 kiosk, the K8 faired much worse because the thirty-year rule deemed these kiosks too young to be protected. This is why there are today so few surviving examples of the K8 but, fortunately, most of those that did survive have subsequently been listed and protected.

The telephone within the kiosk also underwent further enhancements. The microprocessor-controlled CT22A Blue payphone was trialled in 1979 within 100 high-revenue earning kiosks before undergoing

A rare survivor of British Telecom's kiosk modernisation programme. This K8, in Hawkesbury Upton, Gloucestershire, is now listed.

wider deployment. Apart from the move to push buttons, this design displayed the remaining credit and at the end of the call could return any unused coins or allow another call to be made. An improved version, the CT24 Blue Payphone 2, was introduced in 1983. A more significant change, however, was the move to cashless payment. British Telecom introduced their Cardphone pre-payment system in 1981, based on a technology developed by Landis+Gyr. These pre-payment cards could be obtained from several high-street outlets and each came pre-loaded with a fixed number of credit units. Card value was based on a 5p unit charge, making a 40-unit card worth £2 and a 200-unit card worth £10 – a welcome alternative to a pocketful of five-pence pieces, as the marketing campaign said. Once inserted within the telephone, an infrared scanner read an optical strip embedded within the card to detect how many units remained. While in use, the card was heated to erase the credit, unit by unit. Shortly after the launch, British Telecom changed the branding of the service from Cardphone to Phonecard and this name started to appear on kiosks that were so equipped.

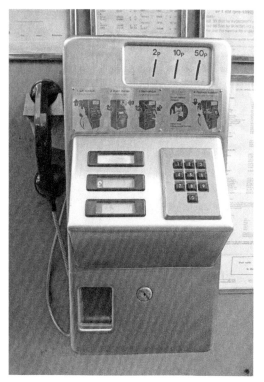 

Above left: The microprocessor-controlled CT22A Blue payphone, introduced into kiosks in 1979.

Above right: The CT24 Blue Payphone 2, introduced into kiosks in 1983.

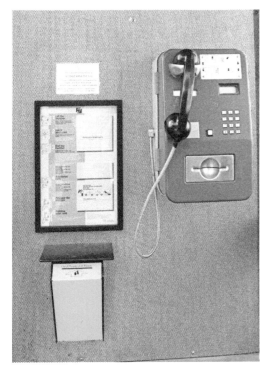 

Above left: The interior of a kiosk able to accept phonecards. Note the horizontal slot for inserting the card and the green box for depositing used cards.

Above right: A Phonecard-branded KX100 kiosk. Note the green horizontal strip on the door and the early British Telecom logo on the side window. This example is on display at Avoncroft Museum of Historic Buildings.

The second series of phonecards onwards also carried this new name and later versions included a notch to help partially sighted people orientate the card correctly. The removal of cash from a kiosk was an important step forward in the battle against vandalism, for a phonecard kiosk was deemed five times less susceptible to attack.

The introduction of phonecards had a further and unexpected consequence. Up until 1987, phonecards were plain green but BT realised that these little pieces of plastic had huge marketing potential and started to release special and commemorative cards. The first of these was for the Open Golf Championship at Muirfield, but was quickly followed by cards for Christmas 1987 and St Valentine's Day 1988. Thereafter, phonecards carried more general-purpose advertising and a whole new industry was spawned. With that came the Fusilatelist: the collector of phonecards! At their height of popularity, limited edition phonecards were changing hands for significantly more money than the credits which they carried. Today, however, the bottom has fallen out of the market and, aside from one of two special cases, they now have little monetary value.

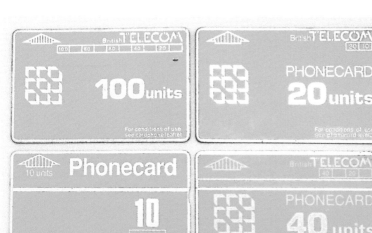

A selection of British Telecom phonecards. The first series of cards carried the Cardphone branding but, as can be seen, this was changed to Phonecard from the second series. Later cards included a notch to aid the partially sighted.

British Telecom's early special edition phonecards for Christmas 1987 and St Valentine's Day 1988, along with more general advertising that was subsequently introduced.

In 1990/91, BT was selling £74 million worth of phonecards per year and, in 1996, the fifteenth anniversary of the BT phonecard was marked by the national launch of the next generation, which used chip technology. Rather fittingly, a limited edition set of cards was produced, with each featuring a KX100 kiosk.

British Telecom's payphone modernisation programme was completed in 1988 and saw a significant improvement in overall reliability. By 1996, 110,000 of the new KX range kiosks were in service across the country and, by 1999, this had grown to 137,000 with an average of 5,000 new units being installed each year. In among this programme of expansion was the KX100 kiosk, installed in the small village of Dunsop Bridge in the Forest of Bowland, Lancashire. Famed for being the geographic centre of Great Britain, it was here that BT chose to install their 100,000th kiosk. Officially opened by Sir Ranulph Fiennes on 29 June 1992, the kiosk contains a commemorative plaque inside and engraving on its windows. Amazingly, in 2008, this kiosk came under threat when BT considered removing it because of its low levels of usage. Fortunately, following objections from local residents and consultation with Ribble Valley Council, these plans were overturned and the KX100 remains *in situ* to be enjoyed by all who visit Dunsop Bridge to this day.

Privatisation of British Telecom didn't just bring about changes to the company, it also transformed Britain's telecommunications landscape through the introduction of commercial competition in the form of Mercury Communications. Mercury Communications Ltd was formed as a joint venture between Barclays Bank, British

BT's new range of chip-enabled phonecards was launched in 1996 to celebrate the fifteenth anniversary of the introduction of the phonecard system.

The KX100 kiosk opened on 29 June 1992 in Dunsop Bridge, Lancashire, to commemorate BT's 100,000th kiosk.

BT's 100,000th kiosk installed at Dunsop Bridge in Lancashire, as commemorated by the engraving on the glass and a plaque inside, which reads, 'You are calling from the BT payphone that marks the centre of Great Britain. It is the 100,000th public payphone to be installed by BT and was officially opened on 29 June 1992. The exact centre of Great Britain and 401 associated islands is at National Grid reference SD 63770 56550 as supplied by Ordnance Survey'.

Petroleum (BP) and Cable and Wireless (C&W). It was licensed in 1982 and became a full Public Telecommunications Operator in 1984, the same year that Barclays and then BP were bought out, leaving full ownership with C&W.

Mercury developed its own national telephone network, over which it could deliver services to customers, and then in August 1987 applied for a license to operate a public call box service. Approval was granted in December 1987, with the first twenty-six payphones being installed at London's Waterloo station, ready for the service to launch on 27 July 1988. Over the coming years, the number of Mercury payphones would grow to more than 4,500.

Mercury payphones only supported payment by either a prepaid telephone card, known as a Mercury-card, or a credit or debit card. None of their payphones would take cash, thereby reducing the costs of managing the service, but also requiring a marketing campaign to educate people on how to use their kiosks. This campaign was fronted by Harry Enfield, and he featured heavily in television commercials and on their range of phonecards. Mercury-cards were initially available in £2, £4 and £10 variants; however, a wider range of variants, starting from fifty pence, was later introduced.

One advantage that Mercury had over British Telecom was that it didn't have to meet a universal service obligation. Therefore, it could pick and choose the most lucrative locations for its payphones, such as city centres, airports, railway stations and shopping malls. However, it was important to distinguish their kiosks and, to do that, three

A leaflet aimed at tourists to the UK, promoting the Mercury payphone service and giving kiosk locations within London.

Above: Examples of Mercury-cards, along with a pin badge that formed part of the Harry Enfield-fronted marketing campaign.

Left: Mercury's ogee-shaped pedestal kiosk, designed by Machin Designs Ltd. This example is on display at Avoncroft Museum of Historic Buildings.

striking designs were introduced, the likes of which had never been seen in Britain.

For indoor sites, Fitch and Company designed a flat totem-pole-style kiosk with a large Mercury logo on its top. The architect John Simpson offered a true neoclassic-designed kiosk comprising four Doric columns, supporting three glazed sides and an open entrance. The roof carried the Mercury logo and name. Finally, Machin Designs Ltd unveiled their pedestal kiosk design, with its large ogee-shaped glass dome that culminated in a small circular Mercury logo. Perhaps these designs were simply too modern, or perhaps too diverse, but the net effect was that they weren't well received by either the media or the Royal Fine Art Commission. Sadly, as far as we know, the only surviving examples of these three kiosk designs are those designed by Machin Designs Ltd. However, all three did feature on Mercury's first issue of phonecards.

In December 1994, Mercury announced its intended withdrawal from its lossmaking payphone business and in July 1995 confirmed that it had sold their 1,500 telephone kiosk sites to the Italian IPM Communications Ltd, who traded in the UK as Interphone.

Of course, telecommunication companies weren't the only organisations who introduced iconic phoneboxes into Britain's landscape, and so our book wouldn't be complete without a brief look at those kiosk designs introduced by the emergency services and motoring organisations.

Mercury's first issue of phonecards, which each featured one of the three kiosk designs, were unveiled to great fanfare in 1988, but sadly were not well received by the media or Royal Fine Art Commission.

Chapter Five

Calling for Help

The previous chapters have examined the development of the British phonebox from the point of view of the telecommunications companies. However, there was another group of organisations that provided phoneboxes and these were the emergency services and motoring organisations who wanted to provide a means by which the public could easily contact them and call for help. While these phoneboxes have long since been abandoned, they do nonetheless represent an important part of the country's telecommunications heritage, with one specific design truly becoming world famous.

The County and Borough Police Act of 1856 made policing compulsory throughout England and Wales but, in those early days, effective policing relied upon large numbers of officers pounding the beat and being visible. Reporting a crime or seeking help therefore required a member of the public to either intercept a passing police officer or report in person to the nearest police station.

In many cases, especially when reporting a fire, time was of the essence and so new ways of providing the public with better access to the emergency services were needed. In the 1850s, the first fire-alarm systems were introduced in America, based on the principles of the electrical telegraph. Here, metal boxes, called alarm or signal call points, were placed on street corners. Inside the box was a wheel or handle, and turning the wheel, or pulling the handle, drove a spring-loaded mechanism that sent a specific number of electrical pulses along a wire connecting that box to the local fire station. At the fire station, the received electrical pulses activated an alarm and were inputted to a mechanical printing system. Because each box sent a different number of pulses, it was immediately obvious from the printer at the fire station which box had been activated and therefore the rough location of the fire.

The first system of this type installed within the UK is believed to be that provided by the Glasgow Fire Brigade in 1878. A total of eighty-two alarm points were placed throughout the city. However, this system had the added advantage that, on arrival at the scene, a fire officer could plug a Morse key into the activated alarm point and communicate with the fire station. In 1891 the City of Glasgow continued their pioneering ways through the introduction of the police and fire telephone signal box system. Fourteen ornamental, hexagonal, cast-iron boxes, complete with a large gaslight on the roof, were erected. These were connected via telephone lines so that police officers could open the boxes and communicate with the police station. Alternatively, a signal could be sent from the police station that ignited the gaslight to attract the attention of a passing police officer.

Other police forces around the country experimented with their own equivalent systems but it is generally regarded that Frederick J. Crawley, chief constable of the Sunderland County Borough Police, introduced the first fully integrated police box system in 1923. He had estimated that up to a quarter of a police officer's shift was wasted walking to and from the police station and their beat. His solution was to erect twenty-two green painted wooden kiosks, measuring approximately 4 feet square, around the city. Acting as a miniature police station, each was provided with a desk, stool, electric light and telephone, thereby enabling a police officer to carry out most of his duties from the kiosk, including reporting on and off duty. This in turn allowed the chief constable to close some of the existing smaller police stations, reorganise the beats of his officers, deliver substantial cost reductions and provide a guaranteed response time of five minutes. The public could also use the telephone, which was accessible from a cupboard on the outside of the kiosk. Fire and ambulance services were incorporated into the system, with the telephone operator at the police station being able to connect calls as appropriate.

Inevitably standardisation soon followed and, in 1932, the GPO announced their PA1 Police Pillar. These cast-iron posts had a triangular head with a light on top. On the column of the pillar was a first aid box and then, within the head, two telephones. A loudspeaker phone, activated by opening a spring-loaded door, was for public use, whereas the other, which was behind a locked door, was for police use. The light was illuminated whenever a member of the public was making a call, or it could be flashed if the police station needed to attract the attention of a police officer. These pillars, in keeping with GPO policy for their kiosks, were painted red and, by 1935, thirty-two police forces had introduced them, with a further nine planned.

In London, Gilbert MacKenzie Trench, architect and surveyor of the Metropolitan Police, designed an alternative Police Pillar in 1937. This was a rectangular cast-iron post that contained a conventional telephone handset, rather than a loudspeaker phone, and a storage compartment. Another compartment immediately below the telephone opened to form a writing shelf. On top of the pillar's curved roof was a light within a metal housing. A version of this design was adopted by the GPO in 1954 and marketed as their PA2 Police Pillar. A lighter version of the PA2, designated the PA3, became standard issue from 1958. Interestingly, while in 1929 the police forces reaffirmed their support that pillars should be painted red, this was overturned in 1948 when they opted for blue instead. Metropolitan Police pillars were painted dark blue, whereas those used by the City of London Police forces were light blue.

Telephone pillars were ideal for providing call points where space was at a premium, but they were limited in function. A kiosk, on the other hand, offered a police officer a place to work, a place to interact with the public and, when necessary, a place in which to lock-up criminals until transport arrived! Initially kiosks were made from wood, with designs varying from region to region; however, some unusual examples also appeared, such as the kiosk opened in 1928 and located within a stone pillar in Trafalgar Square, London. However, it was the 1929-designed kiosk, introduced by the Metropolitan Police, that has become Britain's most recognisable police box. Designed by Gilbert MacKenzie Trench, his police box was 4 feet 6 inches square and 9 feet 4 inches tall; it was made from reinforced concrete, with a stepped pyramidal roof topped off with a light. Accessible from

Above left: GPO PA1 Police Pillar. This example is on display at Avoncroft Museum of Historic Buildings.

Above right: A police officer using a Metropolitan Police Telephone Pillar. (BT Heritage and Archives)

Above: The Metropolitan Police and GPO PA2 and PA3 Police Pillars all included a conventional telephone handset rather than a loud-speaker telephone. This example is on display at Avoncroft Museum of Historic Buildings.

Right: A surviving but disused Police Telephone Pillar at St Martin's Le Grande, EC1, London.

A wooden police box (kiosk) from Coventry, now preserved and on display at Avoncroft Museum of Historic Buildings.

The 1928 police box located within a stone pillar at Trafalgar Square, London.

A blue, Glasgow, concrete police box, forming part of the National Telephone Kiosk collection at Avoncroft Museum of Historic Buidings.

The interior of a police box, showing the desk and stool used by the police officer.

The stepped pyramidal roof of a police box, showing the illuminated light that was activated by the police station to draw the attention of a nearby police officer.

outside was a first aid kit and public telephone for making emergency calls. Inside there was a table, stool and telephone for use by a police officer. As with other police kiosks, the light on the roof could be illuminated by the police station to draw the attention of any passing police officers. This design evolved through two further iterations. A mark 2 version had minor changes to the signage and positioning of the first aid box, whereas a version introduced in Glasgow could be distinguished by the fact that the door had three panels, not four, and was painted red, not blue. However, from Saturday 23 November 1963 onwards, the mark 2 police box was destined to achieve global and lasting fame as the time machine used by a certain Time Lord. From William Hartnell to Peter Capaldi, the Doctor's TARDIS has remained locked in the form of a British police box because of a malfunction in its chameleon circuit. Nevertheless, there is one important difference between the TARDIS and the mark 2 police box, to which the authors can testify, and that is, rather than being bigger on the inside, the interior of a mark 2 police box is slightly smaller than its exterior!

Over 1,000 police boxes were erected in London and Glasgow alone; however, in 1937 the introduction of the world's first emergency telephone number in the UK, the so-called 999 service, meant that people could now call for help from any telephone kiosk. In areas where the local exchange was still manually operated, kiosks included an emergency call button just above the telephone.

A growing use of personal mobile radio systems by police forces in the 1960s to communicate with their officers meant that the usage and need for police boxes diminished – the last operational one was removed from London in 1981. From 2000, the UK emergency services switched to the digital Terrestrial Trunked Radio (TETRA) system provided by Airwave. However, this system itself is now due to be replaced in the middle of 2017 with the launch of the new 4G-based emergency services network being provided by the mobile operator EE, which is now part of BT.

Moving on now to the motoring organisations, the Royal Automobile Club was formed in 1897 and, eight years later, the Automobile Association came into existence. With car ownership growing, both organisations expanded their fledgling roadside-assistance services and patrols. In 1912 each introduced their first wooden roadside sentry box kiosks. Initially these were intended simply to provide shelter for their patrolmen, who could offer mechanical assistance, directions and even first aid. Each box was individually numbered and subsequently provided with a telephone, not only for the patrolman's use, but for members too. In 1920 the AA started issuing members with keys to open boxes; often only the upper portion could

In areas where the local telephone exchange was manually operated, kiosks were fitted with an emergency call button. Pressing this alerted the operator that you wanted to call for either fire, police or ambulance services.

be opened to gain access to the telephone. However, unlike police boxes, which only allowed emergency calls, when first introduced members could call other numbers from AA and RAC boxes. Honesty boxes were included to take the money and you were expected to make a record of your call in a notebook.

By 1938, the AA had 638 kiosks throughout the UK and, in 1947, the keys to RAC and AA boxes became interchangeable. In 1968 AA wooden kiosks, which had peaked at 787, began to be phased out, to be replaced by pedestal kiosks, except for those that were listed or located in areas of scenic beauty. Then in 1992 new pillar designs were introduced. Similarly, the RAC, which had over 500 of its own wooden kiosks, did likewise.

In the mid-1990s, mobile phone ownership was starting to grow and both the RAC and AA introduced their own branded phones. The AA Callsafe Bag Phone from 1994 was connected to Vodafone's mobile network but was intended purely as an emergency phone, providing only two dialling options: one to connect to the AA and the other for 999 services.

The RAC closed its network of emergency phones in 1996, with the AA following suit in 2002, reporting that they accounted for only 0.1 per cent of calls received. Today, both organisations communicate with their members via smartphone apps.

So, while the emergency services and motoring organisations abandoned their phoneboxes, the telecommunication companies sought to keep theirs, despite growing pressure from the mobile phone.

An AA wooden sentry box, which was first introduced in 1912. This example is on display at Avoncroft Museum of Historic Buildings.

A later and possibly more recognisable AA roadside phonebox. This example is preserved at Amberley Museum and Heritage Centre. (Neil Johannessen)

A wooden RAC sentry box, designed by Felix Hudlass and introduced from 1912. This example is on display at Avoncroft Museum of Historic Buildings.

A wooden RAC sentry box of unusual design on display at the Buckinghamshire Railway Centre.

A later design of RAC wooden sentry box, introduced in the 1930s. This example is on display at the British Motor Museum at Gaydon.

Above left: An AA pedestal kiosk, introduced to replace their wooden kiosks. This example is on display at Avoncroft Museum of Historic Buildings.

Above right: A shared-service AA pedestal kiosk with call buttons for contacting the AA or RAC, calling 999 or for non-member breakdown. This example is on display at Avoncroft Museum of Historic Buildings.

Right: An AA Guardsman pillar kiosk, which could be connected to the AA's network either by a landline telephone circuit or via a mobile phone connection through an antenna mounted within the column. This example is on display at Avoncroft Museum of Historic Buildings.

Above left: An unusual and rather unsuccessful pedestal kiosk introduced by the RAC. People complained that they couldn't hear and found it awkward to bend down to the correct position to use it. This example is on display at Avoncroft Museum of Historic Buildings.

Above right: An RAC pedestal kiosk. This example is on display at Avoncroft Museum of Historic Buildings.

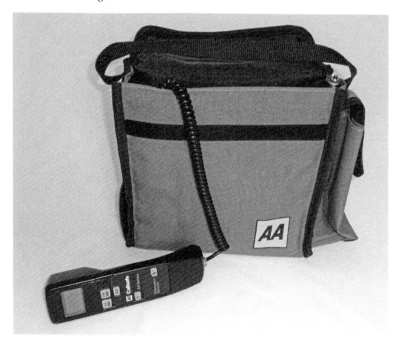

An AA Callsafe Bag Phone from 1994. This was connected to Vodafone's ETACS analogue network and allowed members to either call the AA or the emergency services only.

Chapter Six

The Kiosk under Threat

The mid-1990s proved to be the pinnacle of Britain's phoneboxes. Ten years earlier in 1985, the first two UK mobile phone operators had opened for business and, while mobile phone ownership only stood at 7 per cent of the population by 1995, this was set to change dramatically towards the turn of the century.

Despite the impending threat from the mobile, in the mid-1990s companies continued to see a future in public phoneboxes. Excluding Hull, which was the exclusive domain of Kingston Communications, the two existing providers of public kiosks – BT and Interphone – were joined by a third, New World Payphones, which was granted an operator's licence on 5 February 1996. By 1996, the UK's installed base of payphones was the highest in Europe at 1.9 per 1,000 population. BT was dominant, having massively expanded their number of public call boxes from 70,000 in 1984 to around 132,000, with a corresponding improvement in reliability, meaning that 95 per cent were always in good working order. These operators and some much smaller ones also provided private payphones in places such as airports, hotels, motorway service stations and shopping malls, where access by the public was potentially more restricted compared to a kiosk placed on the public highway or high street. However, BT and Kingston Communications continued to have a universal-service obligation forcing them to operate unprofitable sites, whereas Interphone and New World Payphones were free to cherry-pick where they placed their phoneboxes.

Interphone replaced the old Mercury kiosk designs, which they had acquired with their own new and somewhat more traditional flat-roofed, rectangular, glass-panelled, grey-and-orange designs. They grew their kiosk empire to around 1,500 installed units, including some that were painted in black and orange and had a rather unusual glass-canopied booth design. Unfortunately, Interphone's business struggled, with their kiosks suffering from poor maintenance and vandalism. In 2000 Interphone was sold to Infolines Limited, who subsequently sold their kiosks on to Central Payphones, who branded the kiosks as Interphone Public Networks. In 2004 most of these kiosks were sold to NWP Spectrum, who invested £2 million in replacing the Interphone kiosks with their own designs and decommissioning unwanted sites. Approximately 150 sites were retained, trading as Infolines Public Networks Limited, but these have now been taken over by Infocus Public Networks. Infocus currently operate a network

A BT public payphone
provided within a
shopping mall.

of unusual kiosks that are both solar powered and connected to
the national telephone network via a mobile link. These kiosks are
designed especially for wheelchair access and, as such, are some of the
largest on Britain's streets, measuring 1.4 metres by 1.2 metres, and
2.5 metres in height. From a heritage point of view, it is nice to see
that at least one of Infocus's kiosks in Manchester retains evidence of
its history as Interphone.

The British company New World Payphones was established in
1991 and was granted its licence to provide public payphones in
1996. However, the company immediately found itself in dispute with
BT when it wanted to use the K2 and K6 designs in certain parts of
London. BT responded to this in the summer of 1996 by securing an
injunction against them, citing grounds that the K2 and K6 kiosk
had strong associations with BT. This was resolved later that year
through a site-sharing agreement in which BT agreed, under certain

circumstances, to relinquish one of its modern kiosk sites and allow New World Payphones to erect one of their modern kiosks in its place. Interestingly, in November 1997, BT went further and agreed to licence use of the K6 kiosk to competitors, providing they painted the kiosk in a colour other than red and ensured that it was evident to the public that it was no longer being operated by BT. That's why you can now see black-painted K6 kiosks in London.

New World Payphones installed the first of their new modern kiosks outside Central Saint Martins College of Art and Design in Southampton Row, Camden, on 27 August 1996. Featuring large glass panels, an inwardly opening bifurcated folding door, and pyramid

Two orange-liveried Interphone kiosks in Hammersmith. (Neil Johannessen)

Above left: Kiosk design used by Infocus Public Networks Ltd, which is solar powered and connected to the national telephone network through a mobile link. This design is also intended to provide easy access for wheelchair users.

Above right: A piece of kiosk heritage can be seen on this phone within an Infocus Public Networks Ltd kiosk in Manchester, where the old Interphone brand is clearly visible.

Left: In November 1997 BT agreed to licence the K6 design to competitors, providing they weren't painted red. A black K6 in London operated by Spectrum Interactive, formerly New World Payphones.

roof, these kiosks were designed and manufactured by MVM as the MVM1000 and appeared on the streets painted bright red with yellow banding and telephone logo. Another design, the MVM7000, was also deployed and this had a single outwardly opening door and a slightly modified roof design and, as far as we can tell, was always painted black. New World Payphones had ambitious plans to roll out their kiosks within Greater London by the end of 1996, and countrywide thereafter, as part of a £15 million investment programme. By 1999 they were operating 1,200 public phoneboxes as Britain's largest independent operator. In 2000 the company became NWP Spectrum, then Spectrum Interactive, before being sold to Arqiva in 2012 for £23.4 million, and subsequently to Clear Channel in 2016.

Coinciding with the launch of New World Payphones, BT unveiled its own new kiosk design on 23 July 1996. Having conducted a customer survey, BT concluded, that while some features of its KX100 range were appreciated, there was scope for improvement in areas such as the need for a more distinctive colour, the inclusion of a seat

Three New World Payphones MVM1000 kiosks with folding doors painted red with yellow banding.

Above: The New World Payphones logo on the side of a MVM1000 kiosk.

Left: A black-painted New World Payphones MVM7000 kiosk. The signage on the roofline also confirms that this kiosk operates as a WiFi hotspot for internet access. Third-party advertising is clearly visible on the door of the kiosk.

and a shapelier design. These were all addressed in the form of the KX100+, which was the culmination of a collaboration between the manufacturer GKN and the design agency DCA. The KX100+ was basically the same size as the KX100, being 890 mm square; however, it was taller, thanks to the inclusion of a Gilbert Scott-inspired domed roof, which increased its height from 2,180 mm to 2,660 mm. A further heritage-inspired feature was the fact that the roof, door and side trim panels were painted red. Accessibility was improved by lowering and lengthening the door handle and through the inclusion of a small seat. Each kiosk was also capable of accepting the full range of payment options, including cash, phonecards and the BT Chargecard, which had been introduced in 1991. An upgrade kit was also produced, which enabled a KX100 to be retrofitted with some KX100+ features, most notably the domed roof. These kiosks were known as the K Excel or KX Minus and can usually be distinguished by the fact that they don't have the new and larger door handle. However, that said, in recent years several strange combinations of KX100 and KX100+ features have been spotted on BT kiosks. Kingston Communications also deployed the KX100+ in Hull but, in keeping with their practice, these kiosks were painted cream, not red.

The KX100+, introduced by BT on 23 July 1996. This quartet is in Coventry.

Comparing the old with the new on the University of Salford campus. A KX100+ in the foreground and a K6 in the distance, showing how the domed roof made its welcome return to BT kiosks in 1996.

In 1999 Britain's phoneboxes were routinely handling 40 million calls per day, with half of all 999 emergency calls coming from them. However, this was also a tipping-point year for mobile phone ownership, which doubled to 46 per cent of the population. Ownership reached 73 per cent the next year and, from then onwards, Britain's kiosks were in trouble. Valiant attempts were made to combat the mobile threat, with posters proclaiming that kiosk call charges were cheaper, a kiosk never had a flat battery, you could hear more clearly inside a kiosk, and you kept dry while phoning from a kiosk. It was also at around this time that BT started to sell advertising space on its kiosks. While this no doubt generated a much-welcomed additional source of income for BT, it did mean that the glass panels on its kiosks would become emblazoned with multicoloured posters promoting a whole range of products and companies. Naturally the other kiosk providers adopted a similar strategy, and such is the proliferation of this advertising today that it is sometimes difficult to discern a modern kiosk from other street clutter.

The 1990s was also a period of change, as more people started accessing the internet from home. In response to this growing trend, in 2002 BT launched a new variant of the KX100+, the internet kiosk. Developed in partnership with Marconi, these kiosks incorporated a NET800 terminal that gave users access to interactive web browsing, text messaging, email and telephony services via a large touchscreen display with integrated keyboard and trackball mouse. These internet kiosks were distinguished

A collection of posters used within kiosks, explaining the virtues of a kiosk over a mobile phone.

A BT KX100+ kiosk, carrying a third-party advert that completely covers the door. Advertising of this form is an important additional source of income for kiosk providers.

79

from their telephone counterparts by being painted blue instead of red. Despite BT having ambitious plans to install 28,000 NET800 terminals in kiosks, railway stations, shopping malls and city centres, the scheme was abandoned in 2006, with only 1,300 units installed. The blue Internet kiosks were refitted as conventional phoneboxes or simply removed.

With the mobile phone revolutionising the way people communicated, such was the demand, especially within London, that mobile operators were finding it difficult to provide sufficient network capability. Clearly, additional capacity had to be created, but that required more densely packed cellular base stations to be installed; this is where phoneboxes came into their own. Phoneboxes provided an ideal place to locate a microcellular base station, and so mobile operator T-Mobile developed an innovative solution based on the Ericsson GSM cellular radio base station (RBS) 2302. While the RBS2302 was small, it certainly couldn't be fitted in all kiosks, but the KX100+ and the modern New World Payphones were suitable. Nicely hidden from view, the kiosk on the street had now become an integral part of the mobile phone network and, while people might

A Marconi NET800 multimedia terminal, offering web browsing, text messaging, email and telephony services.

Above left: A blue-painted KX100+ Internet Kiosk, introduced in 2002. This example is in London but has had its NET800 terminal replaced by a conventional telephone.

Above right: An example of an Ericsson Radio Base Station (RBS) 2302 that, when fitted in the roof space of both the KX100+ and modern New World Payphones kiosks, made them an integral part of the cellular mobile phone network.

not have been using the phone within the kiosk, they probably didn't realise that the mobile in their hand was itself using the phonebox! After a successful trial in 2002, a national rollout started, resulting in 113 of these microcells being installed in kiosks throughout the UK; however, it's fair to say that most were in central London.

Also in October 2002, after twenty-one years, BT stopped selling its pre-paid phonecards. Sales had fallen dramatically from the early 1990s, and customers were clearly favouring the more flexible options offered by the BT Chargecard, and the freedom to use other credit and debit cards. Spectrum Interactive similarly switched from their pre-paid Smartz phonecards to chargecards in 2006.

As a further repositioning of the function provided by a phonebox, in 2003 both BT and NWP Spectrum announced that they were installing public WiFi access points within their kiosks. BT began converting its broadband-enabled kiosks in September 2003 to become Openzone access points. These were selected based on their proximity to hotels, cafes and restaurants, where there was a greater likelihood of people wanting to sit down and send emails or browse the web. Meanwhile NWP Spectrum announced, also in September 2003, that it had entered into an agreement with The Cloud to add WiFi to all of its kiosks.

Sadly, these developments proved to be in vain, for the advance of the mobile phone was unstoppable and by 2004 phonebox usage had halved, with revenue dropping by 40 per cent. While the number of installed phoneboxes had actually doubled during privatisation, by 2001 BT stopped expanding its phonebox network, and from 2002 had begun to identify those that were uneconomical to maintain. That, in turn, led to a widespread cull of phoneboxes, with a consequential significant contraction in numbers down to 72,000 in 2004, with thousands more earmarked for removal. Today the figure stands closer to 46,000 phoneboxes, with BT reporting that usage has fallen by over 90 per cent in the last ten years.

Faced with those facts, you would be forgiven for thinking that Britain's phoneboxes had almost reached the end of their natural lives. However, against all odds, not only have several been given a new lease of life, but companies are continuing to develop new designs for the twenty-first century.

The silver ventilation grille in the domed roof of this KX100+ is evidence that it has equipment fitted to turn it into a WiFi hotspot. The signage confirms that it is part of the BT Openzone network of hotspots, which are now branded as BT WiFi.

Chapter Seven

A Modern Renaissance

Amid the declining usage and large-scale removal of uneconomical kiosks, it is perhaps a little surprising that BT launched a completely new design in 2007. Developed in partnership with JCDecaux, the Street Talk 6 or ST6 is of a vertical slab construction, 1.36 m wide and 2.76 m high, with a public phone on one side protected by a hood and a scrolling advertisement billboard on the other. The first ten of these new ST6 kiosks were installed in Richmond and Ealing, but can now be seen throughout the country. While undoubtedly it is a public payphone located in places where, in the past, a kiosk would have been erected, it would be fair to ask whether the ST6 is truly a phonebox or rather an advert with a phone attached to it? Certainly, that was the view of existing providers of street advertising when the ST6 was first introduced, for they viewed it as in direct competition to their own business.

New designs aside, in 2008 BT came up with an innovative way of managing uneconomical kiosks with the launch of their 'Adopt a Kiosk' scheme. Local communities who were concerned about a kiosk being removed could now agree to buy it from BT for £1.

The Street Talk 6 (ST6) kiosk, introduced in 2007 by BT in partnership with JCDecaux. This example is in Cheltenham.

A Street Talk 6 (ST6) kiosk in London, viewed from the advertising billboard side.

Having done so, the phone within it is disconnected and removed but thereafter communities are free to turn their kiosk to other uses. In our experience, one of the most popular uses is to install defibrillator equipment, which can be made available twenty-four hours a day, seven days a week. These life-saving devices are installed in cabinets within kiosks, which can be accessed via a combination lock. The code to the combination lock is provided after dialling 999 and speaking with an emergency operator, who will ask for the number of the kiosk, which is clearly labelled next to the defibrillator cabinet. Then they will provide advice on how to operate the defibrillator properly. Rather ironically the actual emergency call must be made from a mobile phone if stood within the kiosk, because the public payphone has been removed as part of the process of repurposing the kiosk. In May 2016, BT celebrated the 3,000th kiosk to be adopted by donating a defibrillator for installation by the Community Heartbeat Trust into the K6 kiosk in the village of Loweswater, Cumbria. However, the scheme doesn't just apply to K6 phoneboxes; newer models are also being adopted and converted.

Another popular use is to install shelving and convert the kiosk into a local library or book swap. However, the example in Banbury in

This post-1955 K6 kiosk in Witton-le-Wear, County Durham, is a typical example of those that have been converted to provide a community defibrillator.

Even more modern kiosks, such as this KX300 kiosk in Chipping Norton, Oxfordshire, can be adopted. This one has also been converted into a community defibrillator.

This post-1955 K6 in Hatton, near Warrington, Cheshire, has been converted into a local book swap.

When the K6 kiosk on the right in South Bar Street, Banbury, was converted into a library without permission, the ensuing dispute was eventually resolved when BT agreed to install a second K6 on the left as a purpose-built library.

A K6 kiosk in Cheltenham, which now provides a dual function as a public payphone and ATM cash machine.

The pre-1953 K6 kiosk in Tideswell, Derbyshire, is now a local-history point. (Jack Kirby)

The pre-1953 K6 kiosk, in the village of Shutford, Oxfordshire, has been converted into a nature hub.

This green-painted pre-1953 K6 kiosk on Tottenham Court Road, London, was the first of six converted to provide mobile phone charging points by solarbox. Inaugurated in 2014, solarbox was the brainchild of Kirsty Kenney and Harold Craston, two graduates from the London School of Economics.

Oxfordshire does rather stand out in this regard. In 2014, an unknown benefactor took it upon themselves to install book shelving in the K6 kiosk in South Bar Street without it having been formally adopted. Banbury Town Council were reluctant to adopt the kiosk because it was still being used to make 1,000 calls per year; however, BT were threatening to close it anyway on health and safety grounds unless the books were removed. An amazing compromise was reached in July 2015 when, rather than decommissioning or adopting the existing kiosk, BT agreed to install a second K6 alongside it for use as a library. Surely this must hold the record as the last K6 installed by BT?

With 3,500 kiosks now adopted, the range of alternative uses is very large indeed. These include cash machines, museums, tourist information centres, art galleries, local-history points, nature hubs, an ice-cream parlour, community centres, a pub, a mobile phone repair workshop and mobile phone charging stations. In one of the largest adoption schemes, Cheltenham Borough Council took responsibility for the ten K6 kiosks on the Promenade to give them a new lease of life as art installations. As part of the town's 300th anniversary, the first exhibition opened in 2016 and featured life-size images of some of the characters who put Cheltenham on the map.

A quite unusual kiosk can be found on Southampton Row in Holborn, London. The K6 kiosk has been converted into an art installation known as the Living Box, thanks to artist Andrea Tyrimos. This street art, completed in January 2016, is part of a project with Public Space Jam, which aims to reimagine purposes for disused telephone kiosks. Painted vines hang down from the top of the kiosk, while the foliage at the bottom was inspired by Andrea's experiences during her travels in the Far East. Looking inside the kiosk you'll see stars, which aim to represent the view you would see from that spot, were it not for the haze and pollution of London. The back of the Living Box kiosk has been modified, with the attachment of a climbing garden. Upon completion of the artwork this was a vibrant wall of green foliage; however, a few months later it looked in need of some horticultural attention!

A very popular kiosk can be found in Hampstead Village in North London, where a K6 kiosk has been converted into a coffee shop known as Kape Barako. The kiosk, which opened for business in April 2016, is located on Hampstead High Street and is run by married business partners Umar Khalid and Alona Guerra. Kape Barako is open six days a week and serves a range of hot and cold drinks, along with snacks. Following the theme of food and drink, a K6 kiosk in Bloomsbury Square, Holborn, has been converted into a salad bar, run by Ben Spier of Spier's Salads. The kiosk opened for business in May

The Living Box art installation on Southampton Row in Holborn, London, created by artist Andrea Tyrimos.

Umar Khalid, stood next to his Kape Barako coffee shop, opened in a K6 kiosk in Hampstead Village, North London.

Ben Spier stood next to his K6 salad bar kiosk in Bloomsbury Square, Holborn.

2016 and operates during the summer months, offering a variety of homemade salads and deli dishes, along with cold drinks.

Both Kape Barako coffee kiosk and Spier's salad bar kiosk were made possible by the business owners working with the Red Kiosk Company of Brighton. The Red Kiosk Company worked with BT to develop the concept of reusing old kiosks as retail sites, a concept conceived by Eddie Ottewell and Steve Beeken. Kiosks are available to rent or buy in a range of bespoke configurations, and the first two self-contained food and beverage kiosks opened on New Road, near Pavilion Gardens, Brighton in June 2014.

The red phonebox clearly continues to hold a special place in Britain's heritage. In 2015 the K-series red phonebox was voted top

The pre-1953 K6 on the left and post-1955 K6 on the right have clearly been refurbished and now await their next tenant. Who knows what imaginative plans are afoot?

in a survey to find the best British design, pushing the Spitfire into fourth place. BT currently operates 46,000 working public payphones on Britain's streets, of which around 8,000 are traditional red phoneboxes, most being K6s. Of these, 2,400 kiosks are designated as Grade II-listed buildings; to celebrate the eightieth birthday of the iconic K6 design in October 2016, BT projected giant images onto several of its buildings in London.

But how long can this nostalgia last? For people of a certain age, the red phonebox was an important part of their lives. Before home phones became so common, a phonebox was where you went at a prearranged time each week to call distant relatives. As a teenager, the phonebox provided a safe haven that offered much-sought-after privacy when chatting to your love interest. Maybe you were one of those children who popped into your local phonebox and pressed button B in the hope that some coins might come out? If any of this resonates, then Britain's red phoneboxes were part of your formative years and consequently hold some very personal memories. But what about the younger generation, who have grown up with a phone in their home and who got their first mobile when they were ten? What does the phonebox mean to them? Might they not think we are all a little crazy, lusting after a hunk of cast iron that no one wants to use any more? In twenty or thirty years' time, will they be that bothered about preserving a K2, K4, K6 or a K8? Will they even know what they are or be able to tell the various marks and types apart? The emotional connection simply won't be there; however, maybe instead they'll have an attachment to their old Nokia or BlackBerry.

What is certain, though, is that we'll still have kiosks on our streets; the exciting news, as far as Britain's phoneboxes are concerned, is that new designs are set to appear. Clear Channel, who bought New World Payphones from Arqiva, have teamed up with Amscreen to launch a new range of digital kiosks, featuring a large advertising screen, WiFi access, an interactive display and a payphone. Meanwhile BT have announced a partnership with the technology and media company Intersection and the outdoor advertising company Primesight to introduce ultramodern kiosks called Links. These will provide access to ultrafast WiFi, mobile device charging, interactive maps, directions and local services as well, of course, as offering a public payphone.

So, it can be safely said that, building on its long and illustrious history, the British phonebox is about to open yet another new chapter, one that will hopefully secure its future well into the twenty-first century.

Britain's latest generation of phonebox, created by New World Payphones, manufactured by Amscreen and marketed by Clear Channel. These stylish kiosks satisfy our twenty-first century communications needs while celebrating Britain's kiosk heritage through a Scott-inspired domed roof and side-window arrangement that is reminiscent of the K6 Jubilee kiosk. Each kiosk is fully accessible and combines a public payphone with a WiFi access point, a touch-sensitive interactive display providing local information, and an outward-facing large panel digital advertising screen. (New World Payphones)

Author Biographies

Nigel Linge is Professor of Telecommunications at the University of Salford, with thirty years of experience as a member of academic staff. He also takes a keen interest in the heritage of his subject and has an active public engagement profile, through which he delivers a series of popular general interest talks covering all aspects of telecommunications. Nigel is a chartered engineer and chartered IT professional, and a fellow of the Institution and Engineering and Technology, British Computer Society and the Institute of Telecommunication Professionals. Nigel is also co-author of the book *30 Years of Mobile Phones in the UK*.

Andy Sutton has worked in the UK telecommunications industry for over thirty years. In addition to his interests in the latest technological developments, he has a keen interest in the history of telecommunications. Andy is a chartered engineer and a fellow of the Institution of Engineering and Technology, the British Computer Society and the Institute of Telecommunications Professionals. Andy holds the post of visiting professor at the University of Salford and is a member of the Association for Industrial Archaeology. Andy is co-author of the book *30 Years of Mobile Phones in the UK*.

Also published by Nigel Linge and Andy Sutton

30 Years of Mobile Phones in the UK, (2015), Nigel Linge and Andy Sutton, Amberley Publishing

Further information

For further information on the history of the British Phonebox, the following might be of interest:

The National Telephone Kiosk Collection housed at Avoncroft Museum of Historic Buildings, Stoke Heath, Bromsgrove, Worcestershire, B60 4JR.

Telephone Boxes, (2010), Neil Johannessen, Shire Publications Ltd.

The Rise and Fall of the Police Box, (2011), John Bunker, Brewin Books Ltd.

Telephone Boxes, (1989), Gavin Stamp, Chatto & Windus Ltd.

Requiem for a Red Box, (1989), John Timpson, Pyramid Books.